Peppa Pig

This Peppa Pig book belongs to

....

This book is based on the
TV Series 'Peppa Pig'
'Peppa Pig' is created by
Neville Astley and Mark Baker

Peppa Pig © Astley Baker Davies Ltd/
Entertainment One UK Ltd 2003

www.peppapig.com

Published by Ladybird Books Ltd 2013
A Penguin Company
Penguin Books Ltd, 80 Strand, London, WC2R 0RL, UK
Penguin Books Australia Ltd, 707 Collins Street, Melbourne,
Victoria 3008, Australia
Penguin Books (NZ), 67 Apollo Drive, Rosedale, Auckland 0632,
New Zealand (a divison of Pearson New Zealand Ltd)

Written by Lauren Holowaty

002
Printed in China

ALWAYS LEARNING   PEARSON

Contents

Meet Peppa's Family

Meet Peppa and George's Friends

Here are some of our friends!

Oink!

Oink!

Emily Elephant

Candy Cat

Meow!

Eeooooorrrhhhhhhhh!

Suzy Sheep

Baa!

Edmond Elephant

Eeooooorrrhhhhh!

Zoe Zebra

Brrrrr!

Pedro Pony

Neigh!

Freddy Fox

Rebecca and Richard Rabbit

Yap! Yap!

Danny Dog

Squeak!

Woof! Woof!

Squeak!

The Wishing Well

Grandpa Pig is showing Peppa and George his plants. He is very proud of his garden. "What is this, Grandpa?" asks Peppa.

"It's a weed," replies Grandpa. "A cheeky plant growing in the wrong spot. We must get rid of it!"

"This little plastic gnome is going to live in our garden," says Granny Pig. "His name is Mr Gnome."

"Oh no he isn't!" snorts Grandpa. "I can't have that ugly thing looking at me all day!"

"Peppa and George," says Granny, "do you think Mr Gnome looks ugly?"

"No, Granny," replies Peppa. "I think he looks cute."

"Grunt! Grunt!" agrees George.

"You're outnumbered I'm afraid, Grandpa," cries Granny. "Mr Gnome is staying in the garden!"

Just then, Mr Bull arrives with a truck full of gnomes. "Toot! Toot!"

"Ahhh!" gasps Granny. "Here are all of Mr Gnome's friends."

"Yippee!" cheer Peppa and George together.

Yippee! Yippee!

"Gardens are for plants, not plastic!" Grandpa tells Mr Bull. "We don't want gnomes!"

"But these are Granny's gnomes." says Peppa.

"Oh! It appears we do want gnomes," says Grandpa.

"Okey-dokey," says Mr Bull, tipping the gnomes onto the grass. Clang! Clatter!

Clang! Clatter!

Peppa, George and Granny Pig stare at the enormous pile of gnomes. They make the garden look messy.

"Wow!" says Peppa. "They are lovely."

But Grandpa Pig doesn't think so.

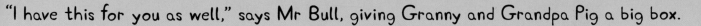

"I have this for you as well," says Mr Bull, giving Granny and Grandpa Pig a big box.

"Thank you, Mr Bull," says Granny. "That must be my plastic well."

"What's the point of a well without water?" asks Grandpa.

"It's a wishing well," says Granny. "You throw a coin into it, and make a wish."

"Do the wishes come true, Granny?" asks Peppa.

"Yes!" says Granny.

"Ooh, can I make a wish?" Peppa asks.

"Of course, Peppa," replies Granny, giving both Peppa and George a coin.

Peppa and George throw their coins into the well and make a wish.

Later, Peppa tells Grandpa Pig what they wished for. "We wished that we could have a wishing well and gnomes in our garden too!"

"Oh," says Grandpa. "I think we can make that wish come true!"

Grandpa Pig drives Peppa and George home to Mummy and Daddy Pig.

"Mummy! Daddy!" cries Peppa. "I made a wish and it came true!"

"What did you wish for, Peppa?" asks Daddy Pig.

"Lots of gnomes and a wishing well for our garden!" cries Peppa.

"I don't think we have enough room for all of those gnomes!" says Mummy Pig, looking at the big pile Grandpa is carrying.

"Nonsense!" replies Grandpa. "You've got plenty of room!"

"Oh," says Daddy Pig, uncertainly. "I suppose we do."

Snort!

Snort!

The gnomes and the wishing well take up the whole of the garden! Peppa and George are very happy. And Grandpa Pig is very happy too, because his garden is not full of gnomes!

Snort!

13

Peppa's Muddy Welly Pots

Grandpa Pig loves planting things in his garden. You can try growing your own plants in some wellington boots just like Peppa's! Ask a grown-up to help you follow these simple instructions.

You will need:

- Old wellies
- Compost soil
- Stones
- Seeds to plant
- Something to make holes in the wellies - a hammer and nail, or a drill
- Water

What seeds to plant:

You could try two different types of seeds, one in each welly. Choose from some of these:

Things you can eat or cook with like cress, tomatoes or strawberries

Or some pretty flowers like sunflowers, pansies or daisies

What to Do

1 Ask a grown-up to make some holes in the bottom of your wellies with a hammer and nail or a drill. This is so that water can drain out of the bottom of them.

2 Cover the bottom of the inside of the wellies with stones.

3 Fill the wellies with compost until you get about 5cm from the top.

4 Press your seeds into the compost.

5 Fill the wellies to the top with more compost.

6 Water the seeds.

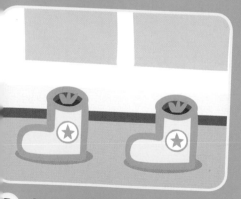

7 Place the wellies in your garden or window-box, where they can get sunlight, and follow the directions on the seed packet to find the best place to put them.

8 Remember to water them every day if it doesn't rain, and check to see if they've grown!

15

Dotty Dot-to-Dot

Join the dots to finish the picture. Then draw a coin for Peppa to throw into the well and help her make a wish!

If you had one wish, what would it be?
Shhh! Don't tell anyone; keep it a secret!

Odd Gnome Out

Peppa has lined up Mr Gnome and his friends in neat little rows.
Can you spot the odd gnome in each row?

Answers: 1. B, 2. A, 3. D, 4. B

How Does Your Garden Grow?

Peppa and George are helping Grandpa Pig plant some vegetables in his garden. Can you help them by drawing in the vegetables?

Grandpa Pig wants to plant:

- ☐ 1 apple tree
- ☐ 2 runner bean plants
- ☐ 3 pumpkins
- ☐ 4 carrots
- ☐ 5 lettuces

Now draw some raindrops to help the plants grow!

Wriggly Wiggly Worms!

Yucky! Peppa and George love finding wriggly worms in Grandpa Pig's garden! Use the number key to colour in this very muddy picture.

1   2   3   4   5   6   7   8

Cupcake Colouring

Daddy Pig and George have baked some cupcakes for Mummy Pig. It's Peppa's job to decorate the cakes. Can you help her?

Add icing, sprinkles, chocolate, cherries or whatever you like to decorate the cupcakes. Make them look as delicious as you can!

Bigger and Smaller

Madame Gazelle is teaching Peppa and her friends at nursery about size. Can you help them draw different bigger and smaller objects on the tables?

Draw something bigger than the ball on the table.

Draw something smaller than the cat on the table.

Draw something bigger than the bucket on the table.

Bouncy Basketballs

Peppa, George and their friends are busy
bouncing basketballs up and down. Boing! Boing!

Can you pretend
to bounce a
basketball too?

 1. How many basketballs are they playing with? **6**

 2. How many cones can you count? **2**

 3. How many friends are there? **9**

 4. How many clouds
are in the sky? **1**

Answers: 1. seven, 2. Two, 3. Nine, 4. One

Castle Maze

Madame Gazelle has taken Peppa and her friends on a school trip to visit a castle. But they're lost in the maze! Can you help them find their way to the castle? Keep an eye out for hedgehogs along the way.

Start

Finish

Hooray! You made it. How many hedgehogs did you spot?

S-s-s-s-slippery Snakes and Ladders!

Peppa and George love playing board games on rainy days, before they go out and jump in muddy puddles! Try playing this fun game, but be careful not to slip on a slippery snake!

FINISH!
32 31 30 29

17 18 19 20

16 15 14 13

START
1 2 3 4

You will need:

- A die or a spinner
- Counters

How to play:

1. You need one or more friends to play.

2. The youngest rolls first. Take it in turns to roll the die and move around the board.

3. If you land on a snake, slide back down to the tip of its tail.

4. If you land on a ladder, climb right to the top!

5. See who can make it to the finish first!

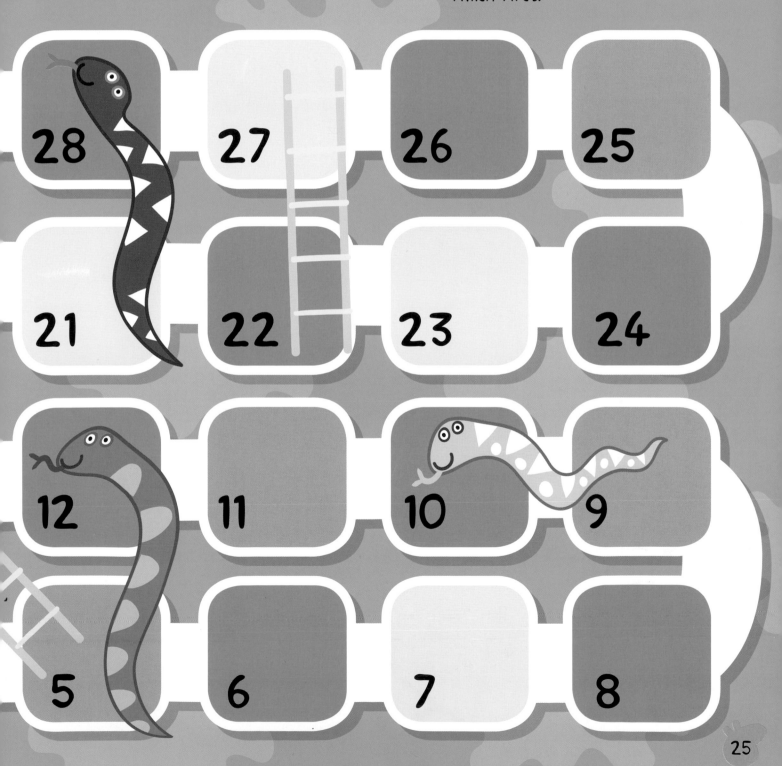

Captain Daddy Dog

Peppa, George and their friends are playing at Danny Dog's house.

"Woof! I'm a sea captain," barks Danny. "I'm sailing my ship around the world!"

"And we are jolly pirates!" cries Peppa. "Arrr!"

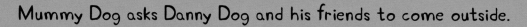

Mummy Dog asks Danny Dog and his friends to come outside.

"Mr Zebra the postman has delivered a postcard from Captain Dog!" says Mummy Dog.

Captain Dog is Danny Dog's daddy.

"He's finished his sailing trip and he's coming home!" explains Mummy Dog.

"Hooray!" cries Danny Dog.

Mummy and Danny Dog are very excited about Captain Dog coming home. "I wonder when he'll be back?" asks Mummy Dog.

Danny Dog and his friends hear a sound coming from the bottom of the hill.

"Hellooooo?" calls Captain Dog.

Hellooooo?

"Daddy's here already!" cheers Danny Dog.

Danny Dog races down the hill.

"Hello, Danny!" says Captain Dog.

"Hello, Daddy!" cries Danny.

27

Hooray!

"How long are you home?" asks Danny,

"Forever!" replies Captain Dog. "I've decided my travelling days are over. I've sailed around the world and made my fortune."

"Hooray!" cheers Danny.

Danny and Captain Dog walk up the hill to see Mummy Dog.

"Mummy Dog, my sweetheart!" says Captain Dog, giving Mummy Dog and Danny a big family hug.

"I really miss you when I'm away," says Captain Dog, "so I'm hanging up my captain's hat for good!"

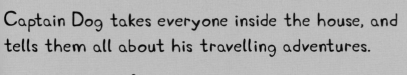

Captain Dog takes everyone inside the house, and tells them all about his travelling adventures.

"I've been away for a year and a day, sailing around the world . . ." he begins.

"All the way around?" asks Danny.

"Yes!" replies Captain Dog.

"What did you do at the bottom of the world?" asks Peppa.

"Did you fall off?" asks Danny.

"No!" says Captain Dog. "I held on tightly! It was an adventure," he says, proudly, imagining himself back at sea.

29

"I've brought presents for you all," says Captain Dog. "Here is a drum for Danny, some seashells for all your friends and a chest of gold and jewels for Mummy Dog."

"Ooh, thank you Captain Dog," everyone says.

"Oh, how lovely," cries Mummy Dog. "Gold and jewels will come in handy."

The next morning, Danny and Captain Dog are up very early.

"I've got a boat that Grandad Dog made for me!" barks Danny. "You could help me sail it at the pond, Daddy."

"That sounds like fun!" says Captain Dog. "Let's get Mummy Dog and go there now."

"Will you be my boat's captain, Daddy?" asks Danny, when they arrive.

"I'd be delighted, Danny," says Captain Dog. "Will you be my firstmate?"

"Yes, please!" cheers Danny.

"Launch the boat!" commands Captain Dog.

"Aye, aye, captain!" replies Danny.

Peppa, George and their friends are at the duck pond too.

"My last adventure was sailing a boat around the world," Captain Dog tells them. "My next adventure is sailing a boat across a duck pond!"

Captain Dog likes sailing across the duck pond. Everyone likes sailing across the duck pond!

Treasure Hunt

Arrr! Peppa and her friends are pirates, searching for gold. Can you help them look for the things on their list of treasure?

Pieces of Eight . . .

Colour in the box next to each thing as you find it in the big picture.

Hooray!
You've found
the treasure!

Bonjour Peppa!

Captain Dog is teaching Danny Dog and Peppa how to say hello in different languages from around the world.

Bonjour!

You can say **"Bonjour"** to say hello in French, just like Peppa's pen pal from France, Delphine Donkey.

You can say **"Ciao!"** to say hello in Italian, just like Gabriella Goat from Italy.

Ciao!

Hello!

Hola!

You can say **"Hola"** to say hello in Spanish.

Practise the words by saying "hello" to your friends and family in a different language every time you see them!

You can say **"Hallo!"** to say hello in German.

Hallo!

Sailor's Snaps

Here are two pictures of Captain Dog sailing around the world.
Can you spot the six differences between them?

Colour in a boat as you spot each difference.

Answers: 1. The sail has changed colour. 2. The flag has disappeared. 3. A bird is flying in the sky. 4. Danny Dog is sailing too! 5. The sea has turned to sand. 6. Another cloud has appeared.

Time for an Adventure!

Ahoy there! Captain Dog has invited you on a sailing adventure! Draw a circle around the things you should take on the boat.

Answers: A telescope, a fishing rod, a lifebelt, a fishing net and a captain's hat.

37

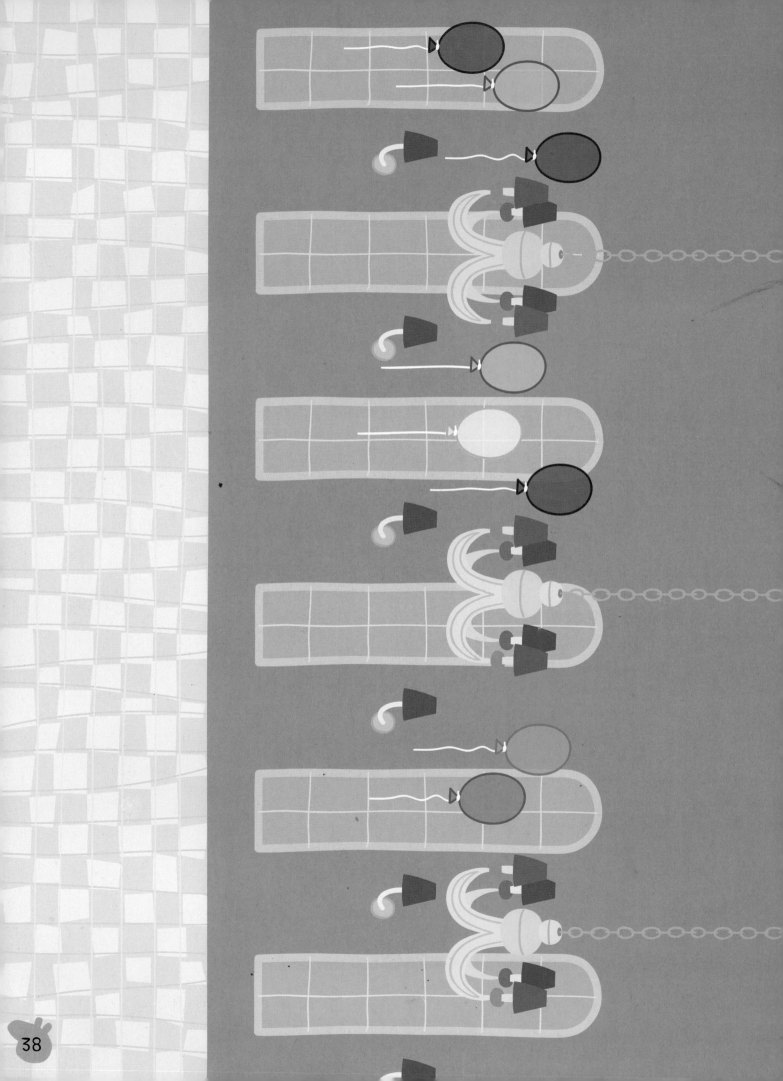

38

Making a Scene

Everyone loves playing musical instruments!
Colour in the pictures on this page, then ask an adult to
help you cut them out and stick them onto the opposite
page to make a musical scene.

Yummy Food!

Can you help Peppa draw what delicious food comes next in each row?
Mmm! Yummy!

1.

2.

3.

4.

P is for Peppa

Peppa Pig's favourite letter is 'p'! Write over the dashed letters below to practise writing the letter 'p' and finish the sentences.

Practise drawing a big letter 'p' in the air with your hand.

This is Princess Peppa

pig

Daddy Pig has a plate of

pizza

George is eating a

pear

Mummy Pig has a

present

Building Sandcastles

George and his friends are building brilliant sandcastles in the sandpit! Can you help them by drawing the tallest sandcastle you can in the space below?

What a Noisy Day!

Read Peppa's very noisy story! When you see a picture, make the sound out loud.

Today, we went to see Granny Pig's very noisy chickens 🐔🐔🐔 ! We jumped into the car 🚗 and put on our seatbelts 🚗 .

On the way, we drove past a really loud fire engine 🚒 and then under a bridge when a train went by 🚂 . We whooshed by a duck pond 🦆🦆🦆 and waved to all the little ducks 🦆🦆🦆 .

Clap your hands!

Cluck! Cluck! Cluck!

Snort!

Brrrooom! Brrrooom!

Clunk, click!

Nee-naw! Nee-naw!

Choo! Choo!

Quack! Quack! Quack!

Cock a doodle do!

Nom, nom, nom. Yummy!

Snore! Snore!

When we got to Granny and Grandpa Pig's house, we were very excited.

"Hooray!" Granny took us out into the garden to meet

her chickens, Jemima, Sarah and Vanessa . When we said hello,

the chickens went to say hello to us. Noisy Neville, the boy

chicken came over to say hello too .

Granny told us that a boy chicken is called a cockerel . Neville

was an extremely noisy cockerel ! After we had a big lunch ,

it was time to go home.

So we said "goodbye" to Granny and Grandpa Pig, then got back in the

car , put our seatbelts on and drove away .

Mummy was driving the car and Daddy fell asleep !

But we drove past a really loud fire engine under the train

bridge and cheered "Hooray!" when we saw the

ducks so Daddy woke up !

"What a noisy day it has been!" said Daddy when we got home.

"I think it's time for bed. I'll read you a bedtime story."

"Hooray!" we cheered . But before Daddy started to read

the story, he was fast asleep in his chair !

"Night, night, Daddy," I whispered, very quietly.

Wow!
What a noisy day
Peppa had. Why don't
you try making up
your own story about
a very noisy day?

45

Muddy Footprints

Peppa and George love jumping in muddy puddles, but they get icky, sticky, muddy footprints everywhere! Help them get home by drawing their muddy footprints all the way up the hill to their house.

Choo! Choo!

Oh no! George's toy trains have come off their tracks! Follow the tracks to help him find them. Then, draw the correct coloured train in each box.

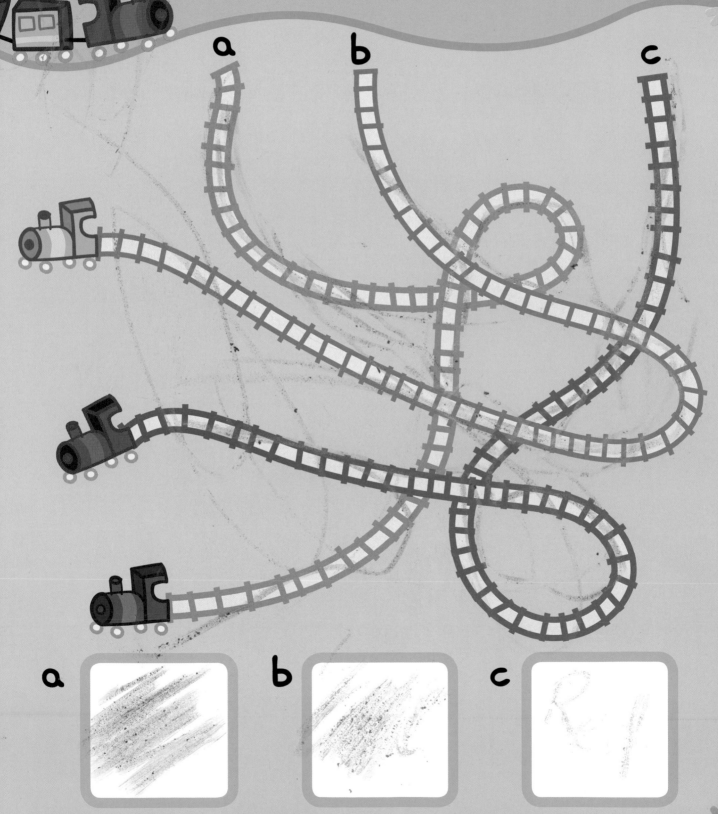

a

b

c

Mr Fox's Shop

Mummy and Daddy Pig are wrapping up a present for
Granny and Grandpa Pig's wedding anniversary. It's a glass vase.

"That's a bit of a boring present," says Peppa.
"Ho, ho!" laughs Daddy Pig. "It's a present for grown-ups."

Peppa and George want to buy Granny and
Grandpa Pig a present too. George gets their piggy
bank to see how much money they have.

"You have one penny and two
buttons to spend," says Daddy Pig.

"Okay,"
says Mummy Pig.
"Let's go shopping!"

Peppa, George, Mummy and Daddy Pig head to Mr Fox's shop with their piggy bank. Peppa is very excited about buying Granny and Grandpa Pig a present. When they arrive, they open Mr Fox's shop door and a bell rings. "Ting-a-ling-ling!"

"Hello there!" says Mr Fox from behind the shop counter. "Can I help you?"

"It's Granny and Grandpa Pig's wedding anniversary," says Mummy Pig.

"They are both very old and need a present," explains Peppa.

"My shop has everything," replies Mr Fox. "I'm sure you'll find something."

"A big teddy!" cries Peppa, picking a teddy bear from the shelf.
"I love it. This can be the present!"

"The present is not for you," says Mummy Pig. "It's for Granny and Grandpa!"

"Oh, yes," says Peppa, disappointed.

"Oh look!" gasps Peppa. "Funny chattery teeth!"

"They're wind-up joke teeth," explains Mr Fox. "Very popular."

"Can they be the present?" asks Peppa.

"I think Granny and Grandpa have all the teeth they need," says Daddy Pig.

"Do your Granny and Grandpa like gardening and digging?" asks Mr Fox.

"Yes," replies Peppa.

"Then why not get them a bucket and spade each?" asks Mr Fox.

"They have spades and buckets, and forks, and everything!" says Peppa.

"I know!" cries Peppa. "Grandpa likes sailing his boat!"

"Say no more," says My Fox. "I have everything a sailor could wish for!"

"Do you have pirates' treasure?" asks Peppa.

"Ah," sighs Mr Fox. "Everything except pirates' treasure."

"Oh," Peppa and George sigh, disappointed.

51

"How about this plastic oak chair?" suggests Mr Fox.

"Is it comfortable?" asks Daddy Pig.

"You can't sit on it!" warns Mr Fox. "You just look at it, because it looks nice."

"That's not much fun," says Peppa. "Even for a grown-up."

"My shop sells everything," says Mr Fox. "There must be something you like?"

"There is!" cries Peppa, picking up the teddy bear again.
"I like this teddy and I think Granny and Grandpa would like it too."

"Ho, ho!" laughs Daddy Pig. "Let's buy the teddy then."

"A very good choice!" says Mr Fox. "Who's going to pay?"
George empties the piggy bank onto the shop counter.

"One penny and two buttons," says Mr Fox. "Here's your change – one button."

"Thank you, Mr Fox," replies Peppa. Then, Peppa and her family
head to Granny and Grandpa's house.

"Happy anniversary!" cheers Mummy Pig, as Granny opens the vase.

"Oh, another glass vase," says Grandpa, not very excited.

"It's a grown-up present," says Peppa. "That's why it's a bit boring."

Then, Granny opens the present from Peppa and George.
"A teddy bear!" she says, delighted. "Thank you, Peppa and George!"

"He's the best present we've ever had! Oink!" grunts Grandpa, very excited!

Perfect Presents!

Granny and Grandpa Pig loved their wedding anniversary presents. Peppa and George like getting presents too! If you could give a present to Peppa, George and their friends, what would it be?

Draw a present next to each friend. Then, draw a circle around the wrapping paper you would like to wrap it in.

Draw a picture of the best present you've ever received here:

55

How Much?

Peppa, George and their family are going shopping again.
Everyone wants to buy something. Can you help Mr Fox,
by telling them how much things cost?

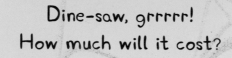

Dine-saw, grrrrr!
How much will it cost?

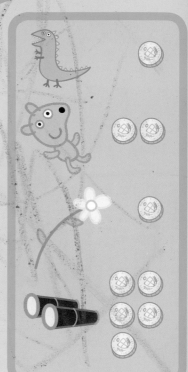

2 teddy bears, please.
How much will they cost?

I would like 1 pair of binoculars.
How much will they cost?

I would like 3 flowers,
please. How much
will they cost?

56

Answers: 1. One penny 2. Four pennies 3. Five pennies 4. Three pennies.

My Favourite Thing

Can you match everyone to their favourite thing?

Draw a picture of your
favourite thing here:

Answers: Peppa likes Teddy, Mummy Pig likes hats and Daddy Pig's favourite thing is his newspaper.

Hide and Seek

Peppa, George and their friends are having lots of fun playing hide and seek in Mr Fox's shop. Can you find all six of them?

Matching Vases

Draw a line to put Granny and Grandpa Pig's vases into matching pairs. Draw a circle around the odd one out.

Answers: The vase with the blue and white flowers is the odd one out.

59

Busy Buzzy Bumble Bees!

Grandpa Pig is explaining how bees collect nectar from flowers and take it to their hives to make it into honey. Colour in this bee picture, using the little picture to help, then pretend to be a bee! Buzz, buzz, buzz!

Goodbye!

It's time to say goodbye. Draw over the dotted lines, then wave goodbye to Peppa and George.

bye

See you again soon.